Start-Off Stories

THE KING'S NEW CLOTHES

By Patricia and Fredrick McKissack

Illustrated by Gwen Connelly

Prepared under the direction of Robert Hillerich, Ph.D.

CHILDRENS PRESS ®

CHICAGO

Library of Congress Cataloging-in-Publication Data

McKissack, Pat, 1944-
  The king's new clothes.

  (Start-off stories)
  Summary: An easy-to-read retelling of the vain
king's experience with two deceitful tailors.
  [1. Fairy tales] I. McKissack, Fredrick.
II. Connelly, Gwen, ill. III. Title. IV. Series.
PZ8.M4594Ki   1987   [E]   86-33422
ISBN 0-516-02365-9

Childrens Press, Chicago

Look!
The King has new clothes.

3

Look! Look!
The King has more new clothes.

4

Look! Look! Look!
The King loves new clothes.

The King has clothes
of many colors.

8

9

But, the King said, "I want more!
I will give gold for new clothes."

Two bad men come
to see the King.

12

13

"Buy our clothes. We want gold . . . gold . . . gold. Smart people can see our clothes. Can you see them?"

15

"Oh? Yes. Yes. I am smart,"
said the King. "I see the clothes.
Here is the gold."

17

The King put on his new clothes.

He said, "Smart people can see my new clothes. Can you see them?"

21

"I am smart. I see the clothes. The clothes are red."

22

25

"I am smart, too.
I see the clothes."

26

"We are all smart. We
see the clothes."

28

Can you see the King's new clothes?

"Not me," said a little boy. "Ha. Ha. Ha. The King has no clothes on!"

30

And, the King and all the
people knew it was so.

31

a	gold	me	see
all	ha	men	smart
am	has	more	so
and	he	my	the
are	here	new	them
bad	his	no	to
blue	I	not	too
boy	is	of	two
but	it	oh	want
buy	king	on	was
can	knew	our	we
clothes	little	people	will
colors	look	put	yellow
come	loves	red	yes
for	many	said	you
give			

The vocabulary of *The King's New Clothes* correlates with the following lists:
Dolch 64%, Hillerich 77%, Durr 72%

About the Authors

Patricia and Fredrick McKissack are freelance writers, editors, and teachers of writing. They are the owners of All-Writing Services, located in Clayton, Missouri. Since 1975, the McKissacks have published numerous magazine articles and stories for juvenile and adult readers. They also have conducted educational and editorial workshops throughout the country. The McKissacks and their three teenage sons live in a large remodeled inner-city home in St. Louis.

About the Artist

Gwen Connelly was born in Chicago in 1952. After studying fine art at the University of Montana, she worked in various areas of commercial art. Since concentrating on children's publishing she has illustrated several story books, as well as contributed to numerous educational programs. Ms. Connelly lives in Highland Park, Illinois, with her husband, two children and four cats.